Bandstand

Barry Maybury

OXFORD UNIVERSITY PRESS 1974

Oxford University Press, Ely House, London W.1

GLASGOW NEW YORK TORONTO MELBOURNE WELLINGTON
CAPE TOWN IBADAN NAIROBI DAR ES SALAAM LUSAKA ADDIS ABABA
DELHI BOMBAY CALCUTTA MADRAS KARACHI LAHORE DACCA
KUALA LUMPUR SINGAPORE HONG KONG TOKYO

By the same author:
Wordscapes, Thoughtshapes, Bandwagon (Oxford University Press)—companion collections of prose and verse
Creative Writing for Juniors (B. T. Batsford Ltd, London)

Filmset in Baskerville by
BAS Printers Limited, Wallop, Hampshire,
and printed in Great Britain at
the University Press, Oxford by
Vivian Ridler, Printer to the University

Contents

page

page

Some of the prose passages are set in a smaller type, and are intended to be read aloud by the teacher.

7 In prehistoric times

In prehistoric times
There was mudday, sploshday, squelchday,
catchday, chaseday, and gobbleday,
There were swampfeasts,
all the dinosaurs came.
There were brontosaurs
And archeoptrixis,
And all sorts of dinosaurs
Came.
They had fissy swamp and roasted dinosaur
meat and hardened dinosaur blood,
And after the feast they all had
a nap in the swamp.
And in those days the world was like
a jelly just turned out of a mould.
And it wobbled and sometimes whole
mountains exploded and came down
like a bomb,
And sometimes the swamps overflowed into
the volcanos and put them out.

GEOFFREY MICHAEL BROWN,
aged 7

When Yondi pushed up the sky

Towards the bottom of the world is a large island named Australia.

The first men who lived in this country were called aborigines. They have their own stories of how the world was formed and how the animals came to be.

These are stories of magic, and like most magic stories they cannot be explained.

The old men who tell them, as they sit round the camp fire, shrug when they come to something for which they can give no logical reason.

It was 'just so' they say.

So do not ask, for instance, why there were rainbows in the land of Yondi before there was any rain. It just was so, for these things happened in the long, long ago when the world was half awake and half asleep.

In the dreamtime . . .

Away in the dreamtime, the world was flat like a dinner plate. There was only a little space between the earth and the sky.

This space was so little it was only the size of a small ant. And everything in the world was the size of the very smallest ant—the men, the trees, the houses. There were no birds because there was no room for them to fly. The animals were very small—so small it took two of them to make a meal for a family.

There was no rain and no clouds. If there had been clouds there would have been rain. And everything in the world was so little that if there had been a rain, it would have washed everyone and everything away.

But there *was* some water. Little pools, no bigger than dew drops, were scattered all over the earth. Some of them were close

together. Some of them were far apart.

One of these pools was different from the others. Somehow it gave great strength to everything in it. It was very precious water . . . and like everything very precious it was difficult to reach.

It was so difficult, in fact, that all men decided it did not exist and did not bother to look for it. Only the animals knew, because animals are wise. If they know there is something they want, they look for it. They don't say it is too far away, or too difficult to find.

So when they were wounded, or when they were hurt, they went to this pool, the Pool of Tomorrow, and washed in the water. And the magic in the water crept deep into their cuts and sores and gently built a cover over them, and healed them. And the animals became stronger than ever.

For many hundreds of years life was like this in the world, then one day a man came to the Pool of Tomorrow. His name was Yondi. Like all other men, he was only as big as an ant.

Yondi was not looking for the pool. He was a young warrior who had been thrown out of his own country for making the

Old Ones of his tribe angry. By the time he came to the pool he was tired and dirty and very, very thirsty for, as I have said, the Pool of Tomorrow was hidden in a place far from any other water.

Yondi drank deep of the waters of the Pool of Tomorrow. And because it tasted so wonderful as it went down his throat, he dived in so that his whole body could be washed.

The magic waters of the Pool of Tomorrow covered his body, soaked into his body, washed his body. They gave all their strength to his body, lifting the tiredness from him, until he felt so wonderful he imagined he was floating.

Then he drank of the waters again, and again, and again. Their strength crept through him until he was stronger than the mightiest tree. And in his heart and mind a great joy and feeling of power grew, so that he wanted to show his strength to all the animals about the pool.

Deep in the water, Yondi found a flat stick. It had been there so long that it, too, had grown strong and hard.

Yondi, the man who was no bigger than a tiny ant, looked at the little space between the earth and the sky.

'I am Yondi, Yondi the Warrior,' he said, 'and it is wrong for a man like me to be so small. I can push up the sky, push it up and up . . . and if I push it up, then I can grow up and up, too.'

He picked up the stick that had been lying in the Pool of Tomorrow for so long and, by stretching, was just able to touch the sky with it. Then he pushed.

And the sky went up.

Then another wonderful thing happened.

As the sky went up, Yondi grew bigger and bigger and stronger and stronger. He pushed so hard with the stick that it bent, but still Yondi kept pushing.

And, all of a sudden, the sky flew right up, high as high. Even as high as it is tonight.

And Yondi sat down and watched in wonder.

For, as the sky flew up, some of the water from the Pool of Tomorrow followed it. And as it got near the sun (which, of course, had grown bigger and bigger as the sky grew bigger) the water started to boil and as it boiled, it turned into steam. The steam formed great, fluffy, white clouds.

From some of the clouds came rain. In some places it rained so much that it filled all the pools that were scattered on the earth. And where there were a lot of pools, close to each other, the water in them overflowed and joined together. And all this water formed the sea.

Because the rain had the strength and the magic of the Pool of Tomorrow, it worked magic wherever it fell.

It touched the trees that were as small as the smallest ant; it touched the bushes that were even tinier. And they grew.

They grew as they are today. They are not all the same size because the magic worked on them in different ways. Some it made as tall as giants . . . like the gum trees. Some it allowed to grow only a little . . . like the small plants from which pansies grow.

Even today the rain has the magic of the Pool of Tomorrow. That is why it makes everything grow.

The men and the women in the world looked up to see where the sky had gone; looked to see where the trees had grown to. And when they saw—they jumped in surprise. They jumped so hard they stretched their little bodies. They stretched so much their bodies would not shrink back to the size of the smallest ant. They stayed as tall as they had jumped.

Today a boy, when he becomes a man, grows as tall as his great-great-great grandfather was, after he had jumped to see what Yondi had done.

Now, when the rain had finished, a great rainbow formed across the sky. A tremendous rainbow, made of all the most wonderful colours that had ever been seen. It grew bigger, and bigger, and bigger, until suddenly it burst into a hundred thousand pieces. And as these pieces came close to the ground . . . they turned into birds.

And that is why birds are so beautiful—because they came from the rainbow.

One animal stood up on his hind legs in astonishment at this sight . . . and ever since has remained standing up in astonishment at the world. He is the KANGAROO.

Another stretched his neck in astonishment and became so frightened he ran, and ran, and ran. And as he ran, his legs grew long. And the bird with the long neck and long legs became the EMU.

But there were some animals that were asleep when Yondi pushed up the sky, so they could not be frightened or shocked at what he had done. And they were lazy, sleepy things anyway, so even when they awoke, and saw all the changes, they were not interested enough to lift their heads to look around.

And these animals have remained creeping and crawling ever since.

And that is the story of how the world grew big.

There is only one more thing. When the sky shot up into the air, Yondi threw away the stick he had used to push it. But the stick was bent—you remember—and every time he threw it away, it came back to him.

So he decided to keep it, for fun, and he called it the BOOMERANG, which means, 'the-stick-that-comes-back-when-I-throw-it'.

ROLAND EGGLESTON

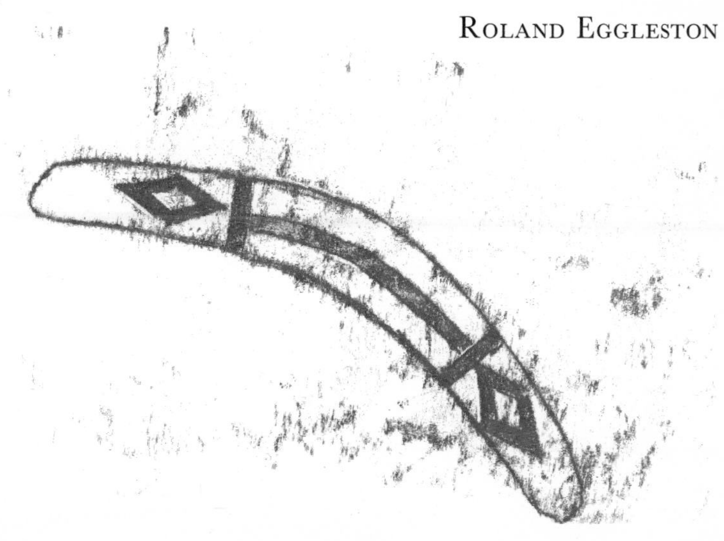

Two by two

The animals went in two by two,
The WALLABY and the KANGAROO,
The WAPITI and the KINKAJOU,
And you!

They couldn't have gone in one by one,
It wouldn't have been the slightest fun,
For what sort of race could you ever run
With one?

They couldn't have gone in three by three,
For the ark must have a ship's company.
They couldn't have gone in four by four,
There wouldn't be room on the main deck floor,
And old mother Noah would shut the door on more.

So the animals went in two by two,
The WALLABY and the KANGAROO,
The WAPITI and the KINKAJOU,
And you!

ANON.

SH1
The Ark

How the whale became

Now God had a little back-garden. In this garden he grew carrots, onions, beans and whatever else he needed for his dinner. It was a fine little garden. The plants were in neat rows, and a tidy fence kept out the animals. God was pleased with it.

One day as he was weeding the carrots he saw a strange thing between the rows. It was no more than an inch long, and it was black. It was like a black shiny bean. At one end it had a little root going into the ground.

'That's very odd,' said God. 'I've never seen one of these before. I wonder what it will grow into.'

So he left it growing.

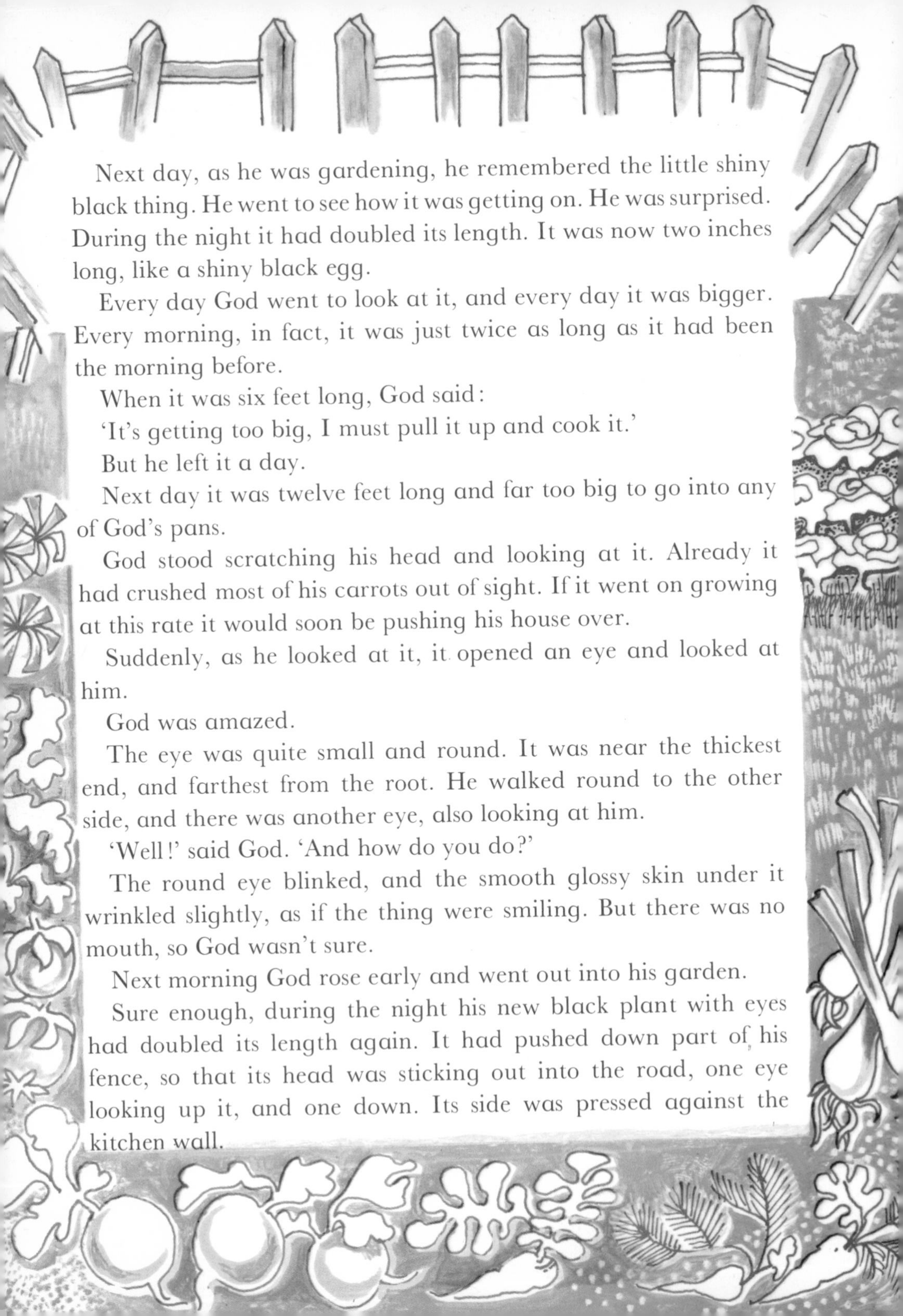

Next day, as he was gardening, he remembered the little shiny black thing. He went to see how it was getting on. He was surprised. During the night it had doubled its length. It was now two inches long, like a shiny black egg.

Every day God went to look at it, and every day it was bigger. Every morning, in fact, it was just twice as long as it had been the morning before.

When it was six feet long, God said:

'It's getting too big, I must pull it up and cook it.'

But he left it a day.

Next day it was twelve feet long and far too big to go into any of God's pans.

God stood scratching his head and looking at it. Already it had crushed most of his carrots out of sight. If it went on growing at this rate it would soon be pushing his house over.

Suddenly, as he looked at it, it opened an eye and looked at him.

God was amazed.

The eye was quite small and round. It was near the thickest end, and farthest from the root. He walked round to the other side, and there was another eye, also looking at him.

'Well!' said God. 'And how do you do?'

The round eye blinked, and the smooth glossy skin under it wrinkled slightly, as if the thing were smiling. But there was no mouth, so God wasn't sure.

Next morning God rose early and went out into his garden.

Sure enough, during the night his new black plant with eyes had doubled its length again. It had pushed down part of his fence, so that its head was sticking out into the road, one eye looking up it, and one down. Its side was pressed against the kitchen wall.

God walked round to its front and looked it in the eye.

'You are too big,' he said sternly. 'Please stop growing before you push my house down.'

To his surprise, the plant opened a mouth. A long slit of a mouth, which ran back on either side under the eyes.

'I can't,' said the mouth.

God didn't know what to say. At last he said:

'Well then, can you tell me what sort of a thing you are? Do you know?'

'I,' said the thing, 'am Whale-Wort. You have heard of Egg-Plant, and Buck-Wheat, and Dog-Daisy. Well, I am Whale-Wort.'

There was nothing God could do about that.

By next morning, Whale-Wort stretched right across the road, and his side had pushed the kitchen wall into the kitchen. He was now longer and fatter than a bus.

When God saw this, he called the creatures together.

'Here's a strange thing,' he said. 'Look at it. What are we going to do with it?'

The creatures walked round Whale-Wort, looking at him. His skin was so shiny they could see their faces in it,

'Leave it,' suggested Ostrich. 'And wait till it dies down.'

'But it might go on growing,' said God. 'Until it covers the whole earth. We shall have to live on its back. Think of that.'

'I suggest,' said Mouse, 'that we throw it into the sea.'

God thought.

'No,' he said at last. 'That's too severe. Let's just leave it for a few days.'

After three more days, God's house was completely flat, and Whale-Wort was as long as a street.

'Now,' said Mouse, 'it is too late to throw it into the sea. Whale-Wort is too big to move.'

But God fastened long thick ropes round him and called up all the creatures to help haul on the ends.

'Hey!' cried Whale-Wort. 'Leave me alone.'

'You are going into the sea,' cried Mouse. 'And it serves you right. Taking up all this space.'

'But I'm happy!' cried Whale-Wort again. 'I'm happy just lying here. Leave me and let me sleep. I was made just to lie and sleep.'

'Into the sea!' cried Mouse.

'No!' cried Whale-Wort.

'Into the sea!' cried all the creatures. And they hauled on the ropes. With a great groan, Whale-Wort's root came out of the ground. He began to thresh and twist, beating down houses and trees with his long root, as the creatures dragged him willy-nilly through the countryside.

At last they got him to the top of a high cliff. With a great shout they rolled him over the edge and into the sea.

'Help! Help!' cried Whale-Wort. 'I shall drown! Please let me come back on land where I can sleep.'

'Not until you're smaller!' shouted God. 'Then you can come back.'

'But how am I to get smaller?' wept Whale-Wort, as he rolled to and fro in the sea. 'Please show me how to get smaller so that I can live on land.'

God bent down from the high cliff and poked Whale-Wort on the top of his head with his finger.

'Ow!' cried Whale-Wort. 'What was that for? You've made a hole. The water will come in.'

'No it won't,' said God. 'But some of you will come out. Now just you start blowing some of yourself out through that hole.'

Whale-Wort blew, and a high jet of spray shot up out of the hole that God had made.

'Now go on blowing,' said God.

Whale-Wort blew and blew. Soon he was quite a bit smaller. As he shrunk, his skin, that had been so tight and glossy, became covered with tiny wrinkles. At last God said to him:

'When you're as small as a cucumber, just give a shout. Then you can come back into my garden. But until then, you shall stay in the sea.'

And God walked away with all his creatures, leaving Whale-Wort rolling and blowing in the sea.

Soon Whale-Wort was down to the size of a bus. But blowing was hard work, and by this time he felt like a sleep. He took a deep breath and sank down to the bottom of the sea for a sleep. Above all, he loved to sleep.

When he awoke he gave a roar of dismay. While he was asleep he had grown back to the length of a street and the fatness of a ship with two funnels.

He rose to the surface as fast as he could and began to blow. Soon he was back down to the size of a lorry. But soon, too, he felt like another sleep. He took a deep breath and sank to the bottom.

When he awoke he was back to the length of a street.

This went on for years. It is still going on.

As fast as Whale-Wort shrinks with blowing, he grows with sleeping. Sometimes, when he is feeling very strong, he gets himself down to the size of a motor-car. But always, before he gets himself down to the size of a cucumber, he remembers how nice it is to sleep. When he wakes, he has grown again.

He longs to come back on land and sleep in the sun, with his root in the earth. But instead of that, he must roll and blow, out on the wild sea. And until he is allowed to come back on land, the creatures call him just Whale.

TED HUGHES

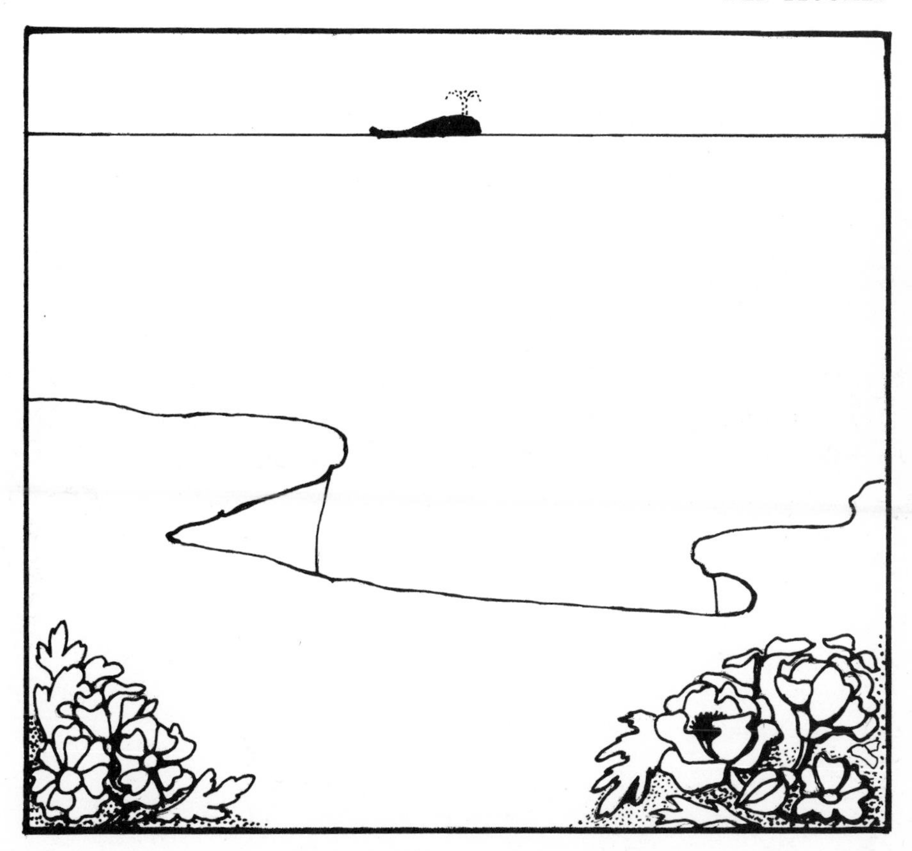

The giraffe who wanted a short neck

There was once a giraffe who loved honey. He had found a broken jar once and had licked the contents out. The giraffe knew that honey came from bees and he also knew that there happened to be some bees in a hollow tree. The only trouble was the hole was low down in the tree and the giraffe had not got enough space to spread his legs out and bend down because he was in a forest. 'If I had a shorter neck I would just have to lick the honey out,' said the giraffe. The giraffe was rather a stupid one and he thought that if he had banged his head against a tree his neck would get shorter. The result was he only made himself dizzy. There was a sprite in the wood who said he would give the giraffe a short neck for a day. The giraffe was ever so pleased, until lunch time. He could not reach his favourite leaves, nor could he reach the grass. He tried to get the honey, but only got stung. He asked the sprite if he could have his neck back and the sprite said yes.

Motto: BE SATISFIED WITH WHAT YOU HAVE GOT!

CHILD, aged 11

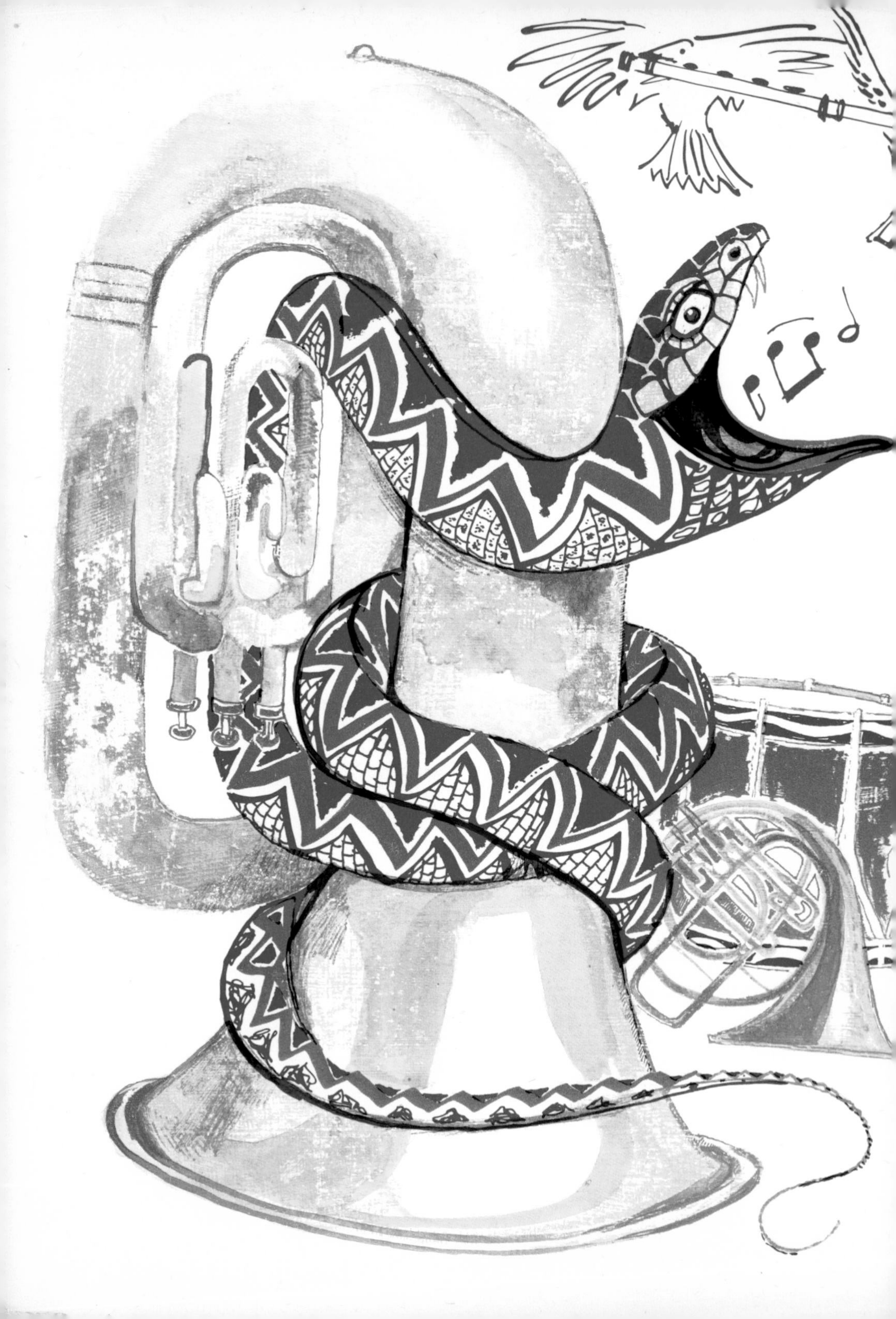

35 The Serpent

There was a Serpent who had to sing.
There was. There was.
He simply gave up Serpenting.
Because. Because.

He didn't like this Kind of Life;
He couldn't find a proper Wife;
He was a Serpent with a soul;
He got no pleasure down his Hole.
And so, of course, he had to Sing,
And Sing he did, like Anything!
The Birds, they were, they were Astounded;
And various Measures Propounded
To stop the Serpent's Awful Racket:
They bought a Drum. He wouldn't Whack it.
They sent,—you always send,—to Cuba
And got a Most Commodius Tuba;
They got a Horn, they got a Flute,
But Nothing would suit.
He said, 'Look, Birds, all this is futile:
I do *not* like to Bang or Tootle.'
And then he cut loose with a Horrible Note
That practically split the Top of his Throat.
'You see,' he said, with a Serpent's Leer,
'I'm Serious about my Singing Career!'
And the Woods Resounded with many a Shriek
As the Birds flew off to the End of Next Week.

THEODORE ROETHKE

The elephant's petals

The elephant was sitting on the hill, looking at the clouds which all looked like very large elephants. Some days they looked like boats, and other days they looked like bushes, but today they looked best. He was very happy looking up until he noticed that the flower was acting rather peculiar.

It kept on walking round him, stopping every now and then and nodding its head, as if it were agreeing with itself about something.

'What's wrong?' asked the elephant.

'It has just occurred to me,' said the flower, 'that you are a freak.'

'A freak!' cried the elephant. 'A *freak*!'

'Yes, a freak,' repeated the flower. 'You haven't got any petals. In fact you don't even possess an ordinary little leaf.'

The elephant had a small think.

'No, you're the freak,' he said. 'You haven't got a trunk.'

'Nonsense,' said the flower. 'I've seen plenty of things

with petals and leaves—like blossoms and creepers and trees and bushes. Why, even the birds sometimes carry leaves—but they don't carry trunks. I've never seen anything with a trunk.'

'What about the trees then?' said the elephant. 'What about *them*? They have trunks.'

'No, they don't,' said the flower. 'They have a very long and very thick stalk, like mine but a lot bigger. Anyway, it's not the same thing.'

'Yes, it is.'

'No, it isn't.'

'Yes, it is. They have leaves and trunks.'

'It isn't the same,' said the flower, getting angry.

'Of course it is,' said the elephant. 'You're just a small tree. More a small tree than I am a small elephant.'

'I'm not,' roared the flower. 'Trees have long wooden stems and you have a small, funny trunk. You're a freak! Try and name me something that has a trunk like yours.'

The elephant tried, but he couldn't. 'Then everything is a freak except me,' he shouted, and he ran down the

hill as fast as he could. When he reached the bottom of the hill and was hidden in the jungle, he could still hear the flower shouting at the top of its voice, 'You're a freak! You've got no petals!'

And that was their first argument. The elephant grew very worried. Not about the argument but about the fact that he had no petals. 'Perhaps I should have some,' he thought. The flower had been very convincing.

Every time the elephant heard one of the jungle creatures coming towards him he scurried away behind a small bush or a large stone and kept very still. He was quite embarrassed about having no petals.

Then the elephant had an idea.

Farther upstream there was a native village.

'I'll go and see the witch-doctor,' thought the elephant.

But even the witch-doctor had no spells for growing petals on elephants, even very tiny ones.

'O well,' thought the elephant. 'I'll just have to go and find some old leaves myself and stick them on me.' And so he did.

The elephant walked round the jungle collecting fallen leaves and petals of all kinds. He made a huge pile of them, much bigger than himself. Then the elephant went and stood under a gum tree until he was all covered over in the messy stuff. Running back to the pile of petals and leaves he jumped into the middle of them, rolling over and over. They all stuck to the elephant.

All this time the flower had been sitting on the hill wondering what the elephant was doing.

'Maybe he's run away for ever,' thought the flower. And that made the flower very miserable. It decided to go and look for the elephant and apologize. After all, it was a silly argument. 'Elephants are elephants and flowers are flowers,' it decided to say when it found the elephant. It wandered down the hill and into the jungle, but it could not find the elephant.

At the edge of a path down which the flower was walking there was a strange little bump, entirely covered in petals and leaves.

'Funny,' thought the flower. 'I've never noticed that before.' It decided to sit on the bump and wait there

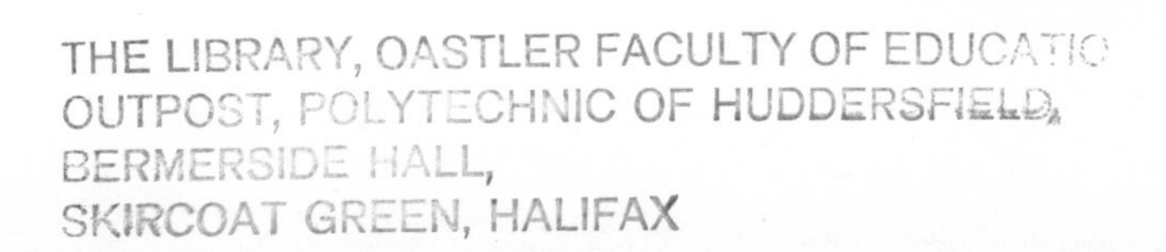

just in case the elephant came past. But, before the flower could sit down, the bump gave a little groan and hurried away.

'That's a strange bump,' thought the flower. 'It's got little fat legs like an elephant. I'd better follow it.'

As the flower walked behind the bump, which did not seem able to see where it was going, it heard it say, 'I'm fed up. I'm very fed up indeed.' Then crash!—the bump banged into a large tree. It staggered about in circles,

groaning all the time. The flower was deciding whether or not to ask the bump where it wanted to go and take it there, when they suddenly came to a shallow pond. Before the flower could shout a warning the bump, still dizzy, staggered in. Splash! went the pond. Groan! went the bump.

When the flower reached the pond it was full of petals and leaves, but there was no bump to be seen anywhere.

In its place was the elephant, up to its neck in water.

'How peculiar,' thought the flower.

'I'm learning how to swim,' lied the elephant.

'That's good,' said the flower. 'I thought you might be drowning yourself because I said you're a freak.'

'Certainly not,' said the elephant. 'I don't like petals on me one bit.'

'That's good,' said the flower. And then it apologized and made a little speech it had prepared, about how elephants didn't need petals after all, and how flowers didn't need trunks either.

The elephant thought it was a marvellous speech and it got up out of the water and went home to look at the clouds again.

Brian Patten

43

Tiger

There should be a tiger in every book,
And just as you're having to sit and look
At eight and one and three times two
And how many's left if I give four to you,
Growling and padding
Straight through the print—
Golden as sunshine,
Striped like a mint—
The tiger comes stalking
Across the page.
Not in a circus,
Not in a cage,
But wandering freely
Right out of the book—
As you sit there amazed
With a dumbfounded look—
Scattering numbers,
Terrifying words
Like dozens of tiny black fluttering birds,
Until he strides majestically proud
Across desks and tables, growling aloud
And sits on the blackboard working his jaws,
Idly licking the chalk off his paws.
And then at last, looking grandly about,
He dissolves in the blackboard
As Miss rubs him out.

JOAN GUEST

The Marrog

My desk's at the back of the class
  And nobody, nobody knows
    I'm a Marrog from Mars
With a body of brass
  And seventeen fingers and toes.

Wouldn't they shriek if they knew
  I've three eyes at the back of my head
  And my hair is bright purple
My nose is deep blue
  And my teeth are half-yellow, half-red.

My five arms are silver, and spiked
  With knives on them sharper than spears.
I could go back right now, if I liked—
  And return in a million light-years.

I could gobble them all
For I'm seven foot tall
  And I'm breathing green flames from my ears.

Wouldn't they yell if they knew,
  If they guessed that a Marrog was here?
Ha-ha, they haven't a clue—
    Or wouldn't they tremble with fear!
'Look, look, a Marrog'
  They'd all scream—and SMACK
The blackboard would fall and the ceiling would crack
  And teacher would faint, I suppose.
But I grin to myself, sitting right at the back
  And nobody, nobody knows.

R. C. Scriven

47

The folk who live in backward town

The folk who live in Backward Town
Are inside out and upside down.
They wear their hats inside their heads
And go to sleep beneath their beds.
They only eat the apple peeling
And take their walks across the ceiling.

MARY ANN HOBERMAN

The pond

A pond's like a mirror
I see my face
Its long its short
Its funny its angry
I ruffle the water
My face has gone.

BILLY BLACKBURN, aged 7

Soap bubbles

Fill the pipe and gently blow,
Watch the bubbles slowly grow.
Toss them lightly in the air,
Floating softly off they go.

High and higher in the sky,
Rainbow coloured, bright and gay,
Every moment growing smaller,
Till they melt and vanish away.

MAISIE COBBY

49

A sea shell

Spin me a sea shell as beautiful as you
are. Spin me a bubble with the beauty and
blue of the ocean.
Sing me a song of the sea.
I saw you lying at my feet I saw a
sea shell on the beach. The sound singing
against the waves with a roar and a
splash disappears.
The sound reminds me of a stormy night
and the waves that splash on the
shore. The shell was a piece of long ago
carved in ancient times with broad shapes
of men.

MARTIN DRUMMOND, aged 8

A deserted beach

Silently the little Crab crawled along the beach,
The wind howls,
The Crab rolls over,
He hits a rock,
The Crab lies still,
There is no movement . . .
He is dead.
The beach is deserted, empty.

Where are the sea-gulls and Oysters?
Where are the Cockles and Mussels?
Where are the Sandcastles?
They have been there,
But now . . . they have gone,
Where have they gone?
Nobody knows . . .
Except the greedy sea.

ROBIN CHARLES SMALLMAN,
aged 8

Grim and gloomy

Oh, grim and gloomy,
So grim and gloomy
Are the caves beneath the sea.
Oh, rare but roomy
And bare and boomy,
Those salt sea caverns be.

Oh, slim and slimy
Or grey and grimy
Are the animals of the sea.
Salt and oozy
And safe and snoozy
The caves where those animals be.

Hark to the shuffling,
Huge and snuffling,
Ravenous, cavernous, great sea-beasts!
But fair and fabulous,
Tintinnabulous,
Gay and fabulous are their feasts.

Ah, but the queen of the sea,
The querulous, perilous sea!
How the curls of her tresses
The pearls on her dresses,
Sway and swirl in the waves,
How cosy and dozy,
How sweet ring-a-rosy
Her bower in the deep-sea caves!

Oh, rare but roomy
And bare and boomy
Those caverns under the sea,
And grave and grandiose,
Safe and sandiose
The dens of her denizens be.

James Reeves

Horses

The horses of the sea
   Rear a foaming crest,
But the horses of the land
   Serve us the best.

The horses of the land
   Munch corn and clover,
While the foaming sea-horses
   Toss and turn over.

CHRISTINA ROSSETTI

55 The magic horse

There once lived a rich merchant who had a fine big garden behind his house, as well as a piece of land which he had planted with corn. One day, while he was strolling in his garden, he noticed that someone had been taking his corn. He resolved to catch the thief and have him punished. He called his three sons, Michael, George, and John, and said, 'There was a thief in my field last night, and he has taken a great deal of my corn. I want you, my sons, to take turns in keeping watch at night. Whoever catches the thief shall be richly rewarded.'

The first night Michael, the eldest son, kept watch. He took pistols and a sharp sword with him, as well as food and drink, wrapped himself in a warm overcoat and settled down under a lilac tree. Soon, however, he was fast asleep, and when he woke up next day he saw that still more of the corn had been taken.

The next evening it was George's turn to keep watch. He also took pistols and a sword with him, together with a stout cudgel and a length of rope. But this good watchman fell asleep like the first, and next morning he found that the thief had been hard at work again.

The third night it was John's turn. He took neither pistols nor sword with him, but gathered a ring of thorns and thistles round about himself. Every time he started to nod the thorns pricked his nose, and he was wide awake instantly. Towards midnight he heard a clippety-clop, clippety-clop, faintly in the distance to begin with, then closer and closer till he could hear it in the field in front of him . . . clippety-clop, clippety-clop.

Quietly John gathered up his rope, pushed the thorns and thistles aside, and crept silently forward. He saw a charming little horse! It allowed John to catch it without difficulty, and it followed him to the stable of its own accord.

Early next morning his brothers woke him. They laughed at him and made fun of him. 'A fine watchman you are!' they taunted. 'You did not even stick to your post through the night!'

So John took his father and his brothers to the stable, where the wonderful horse stood, and no one knew where it had come from or to whom it belonged. It was finely built, and silvery white all over. The father was delighted, and gave it as a reward to John, who called it Corn-robber.

Some time after this the three brothers heard of a beautiful princess who lived, under a magic spell, in a castle on a mountain made of glass. The approach to the castle was so highly polished and so slippery that no one could reach it, but it was said that whoever could ride up to the castle without mishap, and then ride three times round about it, would thus release the princess from the magic spell and win her as his bride. Many young men had already made the attempt, but they had all slipped and fallen, and they lay dead at the foot of the glass mountain.

The three brothers thought they would like to try their luck. Michael and George bought beautiful and powerful steeds, and had them shod with specially sharp horse-shoes, but John saddled his little Corn-robber, and off they set together.

Before long they reached the foot of the glass mountain. The eldest was first to make the attempt, but before he had gone far his horse slipped, and both horse and rider fell to the foot of the mountain, where they both lay still. The same thing happened to George, and both horse and rider came crashing to the bottom and lay where they had fallen. Then John set off up the mountain, clippety-clop, clippety-clop. The horse's hooves rang out cheerfully on the glass, and before long they were at the summit. On they went, clippety-clop, just as if Corn-robber had trotted the same way many times before.

John dismounted at the massive castle door, and it opened to

reveal the most beautiful princess he had ever seen, dressed from head to foot in silk and gold. Full of joy she welcomed him and embraced him. Then she turned to the pony, and said, 'You little scoundrel, running away from me like that! I was allowed an hour's freedom each night, when I could visit the green earth down below, but without you I was unable to get there at all. You must never leave us again!' So John realized that his Corn-robber was the princess's magic pony.

It was not long before his two brothers recovered from their fall, but John never saw them again, for he lived happily with his bride in the magic castle on the glass mountain.

RICHARD BAMBERGER,
trans. JAMES THIN

59 Mary Ann

He's bought a bed and a table too,
A big tin dish for making stew,
A large flat-iron to iron his shirt,
And a flannel, and a scrubbing brush to wash away
  the dirt,
And he's bought a pail and basins three,
A coffee pot, a kettle, and a teapot for tea,
    And a soup bowl and a ladle,
    And a gridiron and a cradle,
And he's going to marry Mary Ann, that's me!
    He's going to marry Mary Ann!

JOSEPH TABRAR

If you don't put your shoes on

If you don't put your shoes on before I count fifteen
then we won't go to the woods to climb the chestnut, one

    But I can't find them.

Two.

    I can't

They're under the sofa, three

    No. O yes.

Four five six

    Stop—they've got knots they've got knots

You should untie the laces when you take your shoes off,
seven

    Will you do one shoe while I do the other
    then?

Eight, but that would be cheating

    Please

Alright

    It always . . .

Nine

    It always sticks—I'll use my teeth

Ten

    It won't it won't. It has—look

Eleven

    I'm not wearing any socks.

Twelve

    Stop counting stop counting. Mum, where are
    my socks, mum?

They're in your shoes. Where you left them.

    I didn't.

61 Thirteen
O they're inside out and upside down and
bundled up
Fourteen
Have you done the knot of the shoe you were . . .
Yes, put it on the right foot
But socks don't have a right and wrong foot
The shoes silly. Fourteen and a half.
I am I am . . . Wait. Don't go to the woods
without me. Look that's one shoe already.
Fourteen and threequarters
There
You haven't tied the bows yet.
We could do them on the way there
No we won't. Fourteen and seven eighths
Help me then. You know I'm not fast at bows.
Fourteen and fifteen sixteenths
A single bow is alright isn't it?
Fifteen. We're off
See I did it. Didn't I?

MICHAEL ROSEN

Song

Huge snowflakes dancing down,
Great hailstones spattering.
At the back door
Dumplings are boiling,
Red beans are seething.
The hunter is returning,
The baby is howling,
And I can't find the ladle—
What a life, what a life!

ANON.

63 The radio men

When I was little more than six
I thought that men must be
Alive inside the radio
To act in plays, or simply blow
Trumpets, or sing to me.

I never got a glimpse of them,
They were so very small.
But I imagined them in there,
Their voices bursting on the air
Through that thin, wooden wall.

ELIZABETH JENNINGS

A wish

I want to climb the santol tree
That grows beside my bedroom window
And get a santol fruit.
I want to climb the tree at night
And get the moon the branches hide.
Then I shall go to bed, my pockets full,
One with fruit, the other with the moon.

TOMAS SANTOS, aged 7

65 The pumpkin

You may not believe it, for hardly could I:
I was cutting a pumpkin to put in a pie,
And on it was written in letters most plain
'You may hack me in slices, but I'll grow again.'

I seized it and sliced it and made no mistake
As, with dough rounded over, I put it to bake:
But soon in the garden as I chanced to walk,
Why there was that pumpkin entire on his stalk!

ROBERT GRAVES

Long, Broad, and Sharpeyes

There was once a king who lived in a splendid palace, perched high on the top of a hill. There were many towers in the palace which was made of white stone, and in each tower there were different rooms. Some were orange or yellow with doors of fine oak polished smooth, some were red or grey with doors covered with leather and studded with bright gems. But there was one room that the prince was not allowed to enter, and that was at the top of the highest tower.

'When I die,' said the King one day to his son. 'You, of course, will be king. Then you may enter the highest tower, but not before.'

After many years the king died and the young prince was crowned. He was very anxious to find out what was in the tower that as a child he had not been allowed to enter. So, one day, when the business of the court had been attended to, he called for the key and made his way to the tall tower.

There were many steps, and it took him a long time to get to the top but at last he managed it. At the top there was a single room. The young king put the key in the lock and turned it. It was very gloomy inside, with old chairs and tables, a spinning-wheel, some swords and spears, and on the wall some pictures, twelve in all. Everything was covered with cobwebs and before he had been in the room more than a few minutes he was covered in dust and strands of cobweb.

The king was disappointed. It was only a lumber-room after all. But before leaving he decided out of curiosity that he would look at the pictures, so after wiping the dust off them he went to examine each in turn. He was surprised to find that in each painting was a pretty girl. Some had golden hair, some had black hair, some had brown hair. But when he came to the last picture he was even more curious, because there was no picture at all—only a dusty mirror. The King removed some of the dust with his hand and peered into the glass. As he did so a shape began to appear. It was that of a beautiful girl and the king could see that she was locked away in a castle. As the picture faded the king saw that the castle was built of iron and that it was beyond the forest and the mountains and a long way away.

The King returned to his rooms and thought about the girl he had seen in the glass, and the more he thought about her the more determined he became that he would find her and set her free.

One morning before dawn the young King set out down the mountain-side and into the forest. The journey was difficult and the King lost his way. So he got off his horse and sat down to think what to do. As he did so something close by him moved and he realised that it was not a tree but a pair of huge legs.

'What on earth—!' began the King. Suddenly the legs began to shrink very rapidly until they were the normal size with a man on top of them.

'*There* you are,' said the man. 'I've been looking for you, Your Majesty. Please let me go with you. You'll find me very useful. My name is Long. Look.' As he spoke he stretched up to the top of a tall pine tree and then came down again with a bird's nest full of eggs.

'Amazing!' said the young King. 'But I can't eat those. Much better if you put them back and look over the trees for the road to the Iron Castle.'

'Easy,' said Long and went up again above the trees. 'That way,' he said pointing ahead.

So the young King and Long set out on the road for the Iron Castle.

When they came to the edge of the forest they found a short, fat man sitting on a stone.

'Ah,' said Long. 'Your Majesty, this is Broad, a friend of mine. If you'd like to let him come with us he will be very helpful.' And turning to his friend he said:

'Show the King what you can do, Broad.' The little fat man smiled and began to grow bigger and bigger until he spread out all over the plain as far as the eye could see.

'Amazing,' said the King. 'I've never seen anything like it in my life! All right, Broad, you can join us. We are off to the Iron Castle.'

Broad came back to his usual size and rubbed his hands happily.

'Delighted, Your Majesty,' he said as a big smile came over his face.

They all three set out across the plain and when they came to the end of it they met a man sitting in the shade of a tree with a black handkerchief over his eyes.

'Hello, Sharpeyes,' said Broad. Sharpeyes raised his head but kept the handkerchief over his eyes.

'This is another companion of ours,' said Long.

'Why is he wearing that handkerchief over his eyes?' asked the King.

'Ah, well, Your Majesty. You see, Sharpeyes has eyes so strong he can see for miles. In fact his eyes are so powerful they can burn a hole in rock. Show the King what you can do, Sharpeyes,' said Long to his friend.

Sharpeyes turned towards a rock that was just a few feet away and removed the handkerchief. He looked steadily at the rock for a few seconds and it began to sizzle and crack, and finally broke up into a pile of crumbling stones.

'Amazing!' said the King. 'Well, you'd better come along too, Sharpeyes. You will be very helpful.'

'Splendid,' said Sharpeyes. 'Haven't had an adventure for ages. Love to come. Where are we going?'

'We are going to the Iron Castle,' said the King. 'To rescue a princess.'

'Good,' agreed Sharpeyes. 'That's just the sort of job I enjoy.'

And off they went. Long would sometimes lift up Sharpeyes over mountains or high above the trees so that he could find the way, and Broad would sometimes stretch himself out across a gorge so that they could all walk over him. The King was very glad that he had three such friendly and helpful companions.

After many days' journey, they came to the Iron Castle. It was dark and forbidding, bound with iron bands and fastened together with great nuts and bolts, and as they walked up the drawbridge there was a tremendous clatter. No sooner were they inside than the drawbridge came up and the gates slammed shut with a mighty clang behind them. In the courtyard there were many statues of young men and horses. The King had never seen so many.

'Very strange,' he said.

'Oh, we know all about the Iron Castle and the Wizard,' said Sharpeyes. 'For many years young men have been trying to rescue the princess, but they all end up the same.'

'What happens to them?' asked the King.

'They get turned to stone,' said Long. 'Sad, isn't it?'

The King nodded his head and wondered whether he too would end up as a stone statue. But he felt happier when he thought of his three friends.

They wandered about the castle but could find no one. At last they came to a room with a large table that was laid with a meal for four people. They were so hungry from their journey that without bothering to look any further they sat down and tucked into the food. There was chicken-pie, roast sucking-pig, bowls of rice, oranges, mangoes, grapes, and the King said he had never had a finer dinner even in his own palace.

Just as they were sitting back resting from their meal and swapping stories the door opened and in came a tall figure dressed in black with three iron bands round his waist, a short grizzly beard and piercing blue eyes. He was grasping the wrist of a girl the King immediately recognised as the one he had seen in the mirror. The sight of her made him bold.

'Let her go at once,' said the young King in a stern voice.

The wizard threw back his head and began to laugh.

'By all means,' he said. 'Here you are.' And he pushed the girl into the room. She smiled pleasantly at the King and his friends but said nothing. 'You may take her away in three days, if you like.'

The four companions looked at each other thinking that perhaps the Wizard wasn't such a bad sort after all. But the Wizard had an evil grin on his face. 'It's quite simple,' he said laughing to himself. 'All you have to do is to keep guard over her for three nights and make sure she is here in the mornings. That's all. But. If you fail—'

'What?' said the King.

'You will all be turned to stone,' said the Wizard. 'Like those other fools in the courtyard.' And with those words he turned, and the door clanged shut behind him so that the sound echoed throughout the castle.

The girl was very happy to be with the four companions but however much the King talked to her he could not get her to answer him. For a long time they all tried to keep awake to guard the princess but finally they fell asleep.

The sun rose up and the birds began to sing and when the King came awake he looked about to discover that the Princess was no longer with them.

'Quick, wake up,' he called to his friends. 'She's gone!'

'Don't worry, Your Majesty,' said Long. 'Sharpeyes will find her out. Onto my back, Sharpeyes,' he said. Sharpeyes climbed onto Long's back and Long began to grow until he was tall enough to look out of the crystal window which was very high up in the castle wall.

'Can you see anything?' asked the King anxiously.

'Far away,' said Sharpeyes. 'It must be a hundred miles—there is a tree, on top of the tree is an acorn and in the acorn is the Princess.'

'Quick, Long,' said the King. 'Carry me there as fast as you can.' Long came down, Sharpeyes climbed from his back and the King got on in his place. They soon clambered out through the window and Long was striding huge distances across rivers, forests and meadows, to the tree. The King seized the acorn and Long strode off back to the Iron Castle. No sooner were they back in the room than the doors opened and the Wizard entered. A smile was beginning to grow on his face but the King produced the acorn and dropped it onto the floor in front of him. As soon as it touched the marble floor it broke open and the princess appeared out of it. At that moment one of the iron bands round the Wizard's waist snapped and fell off with a terrible clang. The Wizard, who was purple with anger, seized the princess and pushed her out of the room, the doors closing behind him.

All through the next day meals appeared regularly on the table and the King and his friends discussed what to do, but they all realised that they must do as the Wizard had said, since his magic was so powerful.

That night the Wizard again entered with the Princess and left her in the room. But though they tried every trick they could think of to keep awake, eventually they all fell asleep.

When they awoke next morning the Princess had gone. Again Long lifted Sharpeyes up to the window.

'Yes, I can see,' said Sharpeyes. 'Two hundred miles away is a rock in the middle of which is a jewel. In that jewel is the princess.' And so once again the King set off on the back of Long across the country. This time they took Sharpeyes with them. When they got to the rock Sharpeyes turned his gaze onto it so that it shattered into a thousand fragments leaving the jewel glowing on the ground. They just had time to return to the castle when the Wizard entered. He was rubbing his hands with glee this time, thinking he had outwitted them. But the King hurled the jewel from the window where he was standing and immediately it broke open and the Princess stepped out of it.

There was a snapping noise and the second band fell from the Wizard. Spluttering with rage he grabbed the Princess and left the room with the doors banging behind him.

The third night they managed to keep awake most of the time but as it drew near to dawn and the sky was growing lighter they all fell asleep. It seemed to the King that he came awake suddenly and looking around for the Princess he realised that she had gone. He woke his companions and again Sharpeyes cast his gaze about the earth. For a long time he was silent, then he said:

'Yes, I think I have it. Three hundred miles away there is a sea. On the bottom of the sea there is a splendid glimmering shell and in that shell there is a gold ring. The Princess is inside that ring.'

This time Long carried both Broad and Sharpeyes as well as the King. It seemed ages but they eventually came to the sea.

'I can see it,' said Sharpeyes. 'There it is, right in the middle.'

Long began to wade out into the sea but it was too deep even for him to reach.

'Stand back a minute,' said Broad. 'This is a job for me, I think.' Broad rolled up his sleeves, puffed himself out, leaned forward and began to drink up the sea. The king watched in astonishment as the sea went down and down and the bottom began to appear. Then they all saw it: the shell glittering right in the middle in the deepest part. Long strode out and was soon back carrying the shell from which they took the ring. Then they set off again, Long taking strides that were greater than ever.

They were just climbing the wall when they heard the door open. The Wizard entered the room as the King was pulling himself up to the window-ledge. The Wizard opened his mouth to speak but before he could do so the King had hurled the ring at the Wizard's feet. It cracked open and the Princess stepped out of it. The third iron band fell with a clatter from his waist to the floor. The King leaped into the room to protect the Princess, but there was no need, for as they all looked on the Wizard began to change like the smoke from a fire until he smouldered into a ball of black feathers from which emerged a beak, legs and wings. He had changed into an old black crow.With a few rough squawks he flew up to the ledge and away, never to be seen again.

The Princess ran to the King and thanked him for saving her.

'But why couldn't you speak before?' he asked.

'That was the spell,' said the princess. 'When the last band on the Wizard's waist fell the spell was broken. Now all the young men who came to try to rescue me will be set free.'

They went out into the courtyard and sure enough the young men were mounting their horses and congratulating the King and his friends on the successful rescue of the Princess.

Long, Broad and Sharpeyes said their farewells though the King invited them to come and live in his castle.

'Very kind of you, your Majesty,' said Long. 'But we must go out into the world. There are more jobs for us to do. Perhaps we shall all meet up again some day.' And after shaking hands with the King and the Princess they each went a different way.

'Well,' said the King. 'That just leaves us. Perhaps we'd better get married and live happily ever after. What do you think?' The Princess who had grown rather fond of the young King agreed.

And they did just that.

ANON.

Doors

An open doors says, 'Come in.'
A shut door says, 'Who are you?'
Shadows and ghosts go through shut doors.
If a door is shut and you want it shut,
  why open it?
If a door is open and you want it open,
  why shut it?
Doors forget but only doors know what it is
  doors forget.

CARL SANDBURG

(Willy Wonka is showing the children round his fantastic chocolate factory.)

On the door it said, INVENTING ROOM—PRIVATE —KEEP OUT. Mr. Wonka took a key from his pocket, leaned over the side of the boat, and put the key in the keyhole.

'*This* is the most important room in the entire factory!' he said. 'All my most secret new inventions are cooking and simmering in here! Old Fickelgruber would give his front teeth to be allowed inside just for three minutes! So would Prodnose and Slugworth and all the other rotten chocolate makers! But now, listen to me! I want no messing about when you go in! No touching, no meddling, and no tasting! Is that agreed?'

'Yes, yes!' the children cried. 'We won't touch a thing!'

'Up to now,' Mr. Wonka said, 'nobody else, not even an Oompa-Loompa, has ever been allowed in here!' He opened the door and stepped out of the boat into the room. The four children and their parents all scrambled after him.

'Don't touch!' shouted Mr. Wonka. 'And don't knock anything over!'

Charlie Bucket stared around the gigantic room in which he now found himself. The place was like a witch's kitchen! All about him black metal pots were boiling and bubbling on huge stoves, and kettles were hissing and pans were sizzling, and strange iron machines were clanking and spluttering, and there were pipes running all over the ceiling and walls, and the whole place was filled with smoke and steam and delicious rich smells.

Mr. Wonka himself had suddenly become even more excited than usual, and anyone could see that this was the room he loved best of all. He was hopping about among the saucepans and the machines like a child among his Christmas presents, not knowing which thing to look at first. He lifted the lid from a huge pot and took a sniff; then he rushed over and dipped a finger into a barrel of sticky yellow stuff and had a taste; then he skipped across to one of the machines and turned half a dozen knobs this way and that; then he peered anxiously through the glass door of a gigantic oven, rubbing his hands and cackling with delight at what he saw inside.

87 Then he ran over to another machine, a small shiny affair that kept going *phut-phut-phut-phut-phut*, and every time it went *phut*, a large green marble dropped out of it into a basket on the floor. At least it looked like a marble.

'Everlasting Gobstoppers!' cried Mr. Wonka proudly. 'They're completely new! I am inventing them for children who are given very little pocket money. You can put an Everlasting Gobstopper in your mouth and you can suck it and suck it and suck it and it will *never* get any smaller!'

ROALD DAHL

89 Engineers

Pistons, valves and wheels and gears
That's the life of engineers
Thumping, clunking engines going,
Hissing steam and whistles blowing.

There's not a place I'd rather be
Than working round machinery,
Listening to that clanking sound
Watching all the wheels go round.

JIMMY GARTHWAITE

The mechanical road mender

Like a giant mechanical monster
As if it would eat the whole road,
It ate—then spat out, with its fat yellow grab,
Its interlocking terrifying caterpillars shook.
The Bowzell crane crushes crunches
and crams.
Its mechanical lever arm
Picked up the gravel and dropped it.
Grrm grrm went the engine,
While the jaws picked up the gravel
and dropped it,
With a ssshhh ssshhh ssshhh sh
sh sh.

NIGEL RAMSDEN, aged 7

A plane

A roar of a jet,
A flare of flame,
Clouds of smoke,
Flashing lights,
Screaming wheels,
Radios cracking,
Plane rising,
Landing wheels up,
Plane getting higher,
With a roar of smoke it's in the clouds
Lights flash off
Lights flash on,
Speakers blaring,
Lights flashing,
With a roar of smoke it disappears.

STUART SEPPLE, aged 8

Let's send a rocket

Ten, nine, eight . . .
Seven, six, five . . .

We'll send up a rocket,
And it will be *live*.

Five, four, three . . .
It's ready to zoom!

We're counting each second,
And soon it will boom!

Get ready for . . . *two*;
Get ready to go . . .

It's *two*—and it's—*one*—
We're OFF! It's ZERO!

KIT PATRICKSON

List of illustrations

Acknowledgements

The author gratefully acknowledges permission to reproduce extracts from the following copyright works:

Richard Bamberger: 'The Magic Horse' from *My First Big Story Book*, trans. James Thin. Reprinted by permission of Chatto & Windus Ltd.; **Maisie Cobby:** 'Soap Bubbles' from *We Play and Grow*. Reprinted by permission of Pitman Publishing, London; **Roland Eggleston:** *When Yondi Pushed up the Sky* (Jonathan Cape Ltd.). Reprinted by permission of Mark Paterson; **Roald Dahl:** *Charlie and the Chocolate Factory*. Copyright 1967. Reprinted by permission of George Allen and Unwin Ltd. and Alfred Knopf; **James Garthwaite:** 'Engineers' from *Puddin' An' Pie*. Copyright © 1929 by Harper and Row, Publishers. Copyright renewed 1957 by Merle Garthwaite. Reprinted by permission of Harper and Row; **Robert Graves:** 'The Pumpkin' from *A Golden Land*. Reprinted by permission of A. P. Watt & Son on behalf of Mr Robert Graves; **Ted Hughes:** *How the Whale Became*. Reprinted by permission of Faber and Faber Ltd.; **Elizabeth Jennings:** 'The Radio Men' from *The Secret Brother*. Reprinted by permission of Macmillan, London and Basingstoke; **Kit Patrickson:** 'Let's Send a Rocket' from *Poems for Me*. Reprinted by permission of the author and Ginn & Co. Ltd.; **Brian Patten:** 'The Elephant's Petals' from *The Elephant and the Flower*. Reprinted by permission of George Allen and Unwin Ltd.; *The Penguin Book of Japanese Verse*, trans. and ed. Geoffrey Bownas and Anthony Thwaite. (Song: 'Huge Snowflakes Dancing Down') Copyright Geoffrey Bownas and Anthony Thwaite, 1964. Reprinted by permission of Penguin Books Ltd.; **James Reeves:** 'Grim and Gloomy' from *The Wandering Moon*. Reprinted by permission of William Heinemann Ltd.; **Theodore Roethke:** 'The Serpent' from *The Collected Poems of Theodore Roethke*. Copyright 1950 by Theodore Roethke. Reprinted by permission of Faber and Faber Ltd. and Doubleday & Company, Inc.; **Carl Sandburg:** 'Doors' from *Complete Poems*. Copyright © 1950 by Carl Sandburg. Reprinted by permission of Harcourt Brace Jovanovich, Inc.; **R. C. Scriven:** 'The Marrog' from B.B.C. *Journeys*, Spring 1968. Reprinted by permission of the author; **Tomas Santos:** 'A Wish' from *Miracles*, ed. Richard Lewis. Copyright Richard Lewis, 1966. Reprinted by permission of Penguin Books Ltd. and Simon & Schuster, Inc.; **Joseph Tabrar:** 'Mary Ann' from B.B.C. *Living Languages*, Summer 1967.

The author would also like to thank the following for permission to reprint their poems and prose pieces:
The Daily Mirror Children's Literary Competition for 'The Pond' by Billy Blackburn (aged 7), 'In Prehistoric Times' by Geoffrey Michael Brown (aged 7), 'A Sea Shell' by Martin Drummond and 'A Deserted Beach' by Robin Charles Smallman (aged 8); Ginn & Co. Ltd. for 'The Mechanical Road Mender' by Nigel Ramsden (aged 7) and 'A Plane' by Stuart Sepple (aged 8) from *Mirror Poems*; The Clarendon Press Oxford and Miss Margaret Spencer for 'The Giraffe who wanted a Short Neck' from *Children Using Language*, ed. Anthony Jones and Jeremy Mulford; Joan Guest for 'Tiger'; and Michael Rosen for 'If you don't put your shoes on'.

Author Index

CHILDREN'S WORK